This book is dedicated to freedom.

A TEMPLAR BOOK

First published in the UK in 1997 by Templar Publishing, an imprint of The Templar Company plc.

Distributed in the UK by Ragged Bears Ltd, Ragged Appleshaw, Andover, Hampshire SP11 9HX.

Devised and produced by The Templar Company plc, Pippbrook Mill, London Road, Dorking, Surrey RH4 1JE,

in association with The Born Free Foundation.

Edited by Richard Widdowes. Designed by Mike Jolley.

This book has been printed and bound by Proost N.V. in Belgium using 100% recycled paper.

No dioxin-producing chlorine is used in the manufacturing process. .

ISBN 1-898784-73-6

WRITTEN BY *Virginia McKenna*
with help from *Will Travers*

Journey to freedom

ILLUSTRATED BY *Nick Mountain*

TEMPLAR
PUBLISHING

Many years ago, the amazing tale of a lioness and two remarkable people touched the hearts of the world. *Born Free*, the story of Elsa and George and Joy Adamson, proved that lions could be loved.

In a story just as remarkable and following in the spirit of *Born Free*, Christian, a little lion cub, was taken from Harrod's pet department, via a spell in the English countryside, back to the freedom of his native Africa. This is his story, one of hope, love and understanding - a story I feel privileged, as with the first, to have been a part of.

Virginia McKenna

VIRGINIA McKENNA
The Born Free Foundation

Journey to Freedom

The pet department of the big London store seemed so noisy to Christian, the two-month old lion cub. The zoo where he had been born had been full of animals too, but they were spread out over a big area. In this one place, dogs whined, parrots squawked, snakes hissed and cats far smaller than him mewed from their nearby cages.

All the smells were mixed up. The natural scent of animals mingled with the smells of wood, straw and all manner of pet foods. In the early morning, before the customers arrived, there was the acid tang left by the cleaners and their humming machines; in the daytime there was the whiff of perfume from well-dressed ladies.

Christian had come to quite like the smells and sounds of his new home. But what he didn't like at all was being cooped up in a cage. He longed to run and jump and climb, but his new home was far too small for that.

One day he looked out through the bars of his cage to find two faces smiling kindly back at him. He was still nervous of humans and moved closer to the back of the cage, crouching and anxious. Minutes later everything went dark and Christian knew that his cage was being moved...

When he could see out again, everything had changed. The smells of the pet department had been replaced by the scent of pine and beeswax polish. The animals had gone too. The little lion looked out at his new world and soon the two smiling faces appeared again.

"Come on John," said one. "Let's give Christian some milk. He must be starving, poor little chap."
"Good idea, Ace," the second replied, reaching for a bowl and heading for the room next door.
Ace and John, Christian's new owners, quickly became his friends.

They fed him, stroked him and played with him for hours. They made him a comfortable "den" in the basement of their furniture shop in London's fashionable Kings Road, but often Christian could be found in the shop itself. He grew quickly and became well-known to the customers who often came to the shop as much to see the lion cub as to buy a desk or a bed.

Sometimes, Christian had to stay in his den downstairs and it was on just such a day, after he had been in his den for quite a time, that he heard his owners' footsteps approaching, followed by another heavier tread.

"Bill, this is Christian," said John, and Christian looked up to see another kindly face looking down at him. This new man seemed more relaxed with him than most humans, stroking and playing with him with no trace of fear in his touch or his gentle voice. Somehow Christian sensed that Bill was a special person, but little did he realise that Bill was about to help him start a journey, one that would eventually return him to the place where he truly belonged. The ride in the van was fun. John and Ace had loaded Christian

into the back of it that morning before setting off through the busy London streets. They had made him a comfy bed in the back where he could stretch out and watch the world speeding by through the windows. Gradually, he saw the jumble of buildings and people thin out to become a view of green fields.

Finally, the van turned into a gateway and came to a stop. The man called Bill opened the big van door along with a lady that he introduced as Ginny. Christian stepped out and sniffed the air. It was fresh and clean, with the scent of flowers. He could hear no cars or people - just the sound of birds and the breeze whispering through the leafy trees.

Ginny led them all down a narrow path and through a gate.
"This is your new home, Christian," she said as everyone filed in.
"And this is your new den," said John, leading the lion cub up some steps to a joyfully decorated wooden caravan.

Christian soon learnt to love living in the countryside. He was happy in his new den, with its large open pen. Ace and John lived right next door in their own special caravan and every day they came to sit, talk and play with him. Ginny brought him huge delicious bones to chew, and Bill strung up an old sack on a rope which Christian spent hours wrestling with.

Journey to Freedom

One special day, they all climbed into the wobbly van and went to a place called the "seaside". The strange salty water and the squish of the sand beneath his paws made Christian run up and down the deserted beach in excitement, pursued by his dear friends John, Ace, Ginny and even Bill, waving a large red balloon. He had never had so much fun.

But back home something had changed. A large wooden box had been put next to his den. Every day John and Ace encouraged Christian to go into the box where they would give him a bowl of milk. At first it was only for a few minutes, but as the days passed they gradually left him in the box for longer and longer.

One day they didn't let him out of the box at all and Christian felt it being moved. For a long time it was dark but, although he couldn't see, the lion cub could hear his friends talking quietly nearby and that stopped him feeling afraid. There were other noises too, and after a while he heard a strange roaring sound and felt a little dizzy before finally dropping off to sleep.

Journey to Freedom

When he was let out of the box he was in a new place, very different from the countryside he had left behind. The first things Christian noticed were the dusty, dry air and the concrete beneath his paws. Nearby, Bill was talking to a man that Christian had not seen before. His name was George.

"It must seem very strange," said Bill, "the idea of bringing a lion back to Africa."

George nodded thoughtfully. Christian liked the look of this new man, with his white hair and thick beard. He liked his smell too - it seemed almost familiar and was somehow reassuring.

This was just as well, because of all Christian's journeys, the one that followed was by far the worst. Lying in an old Land Rover, his friends drove him out through another bustling city. After a while the buildings were replaced with wild bush country and the red earth road became a bumpy track. Dust was everywhere - Christian could feel it filling his eyes, his nose and stinging the back of his throat. And it was so hot!

Journey to Freedom

The uncomfortable journey seemed to last forever but eventually they bumped to a halt and Christian climbed carefully out.

The first thing he noticed was the ground. It was sandy, but not like the beach back in England. This felt harder, gritty and dusty beneath his paws. All around him there were rocks. There were trees and bushes too, but they were grey not green, and the grass was brown, parched by the glaring sun.

Christian raised his head and sniffed the air. Deep in his memory something stirred, a dim recollection from the first few weeks of his life. He recognised the smell that came to him on the wind; a thick, musty, unmistakable smell - the smell of another lion. It took only seconds for Christian's eyes to follow the scent to its source. There on the other side of a high wire fence sat a massive, magnificent male lion. When he saw Christian watching, the lion rose to his feet and let out a deep, rumbling roar.

George knelt down beside Christian who was more curious than frightened,
even though the big lion was more than twice his size.

"That's Boy," explained George, as much to Christian as to the others. "He
comes and goes much as he pleases, but he thinks this camp belongs to him.

 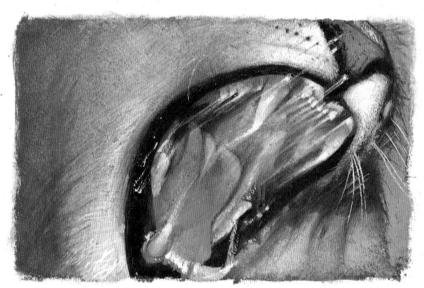

He's not too happy about a new male lion being here, but I hope he gets used
to the idea and they both begin to like each other. In the meantime, we must
all be very careful."

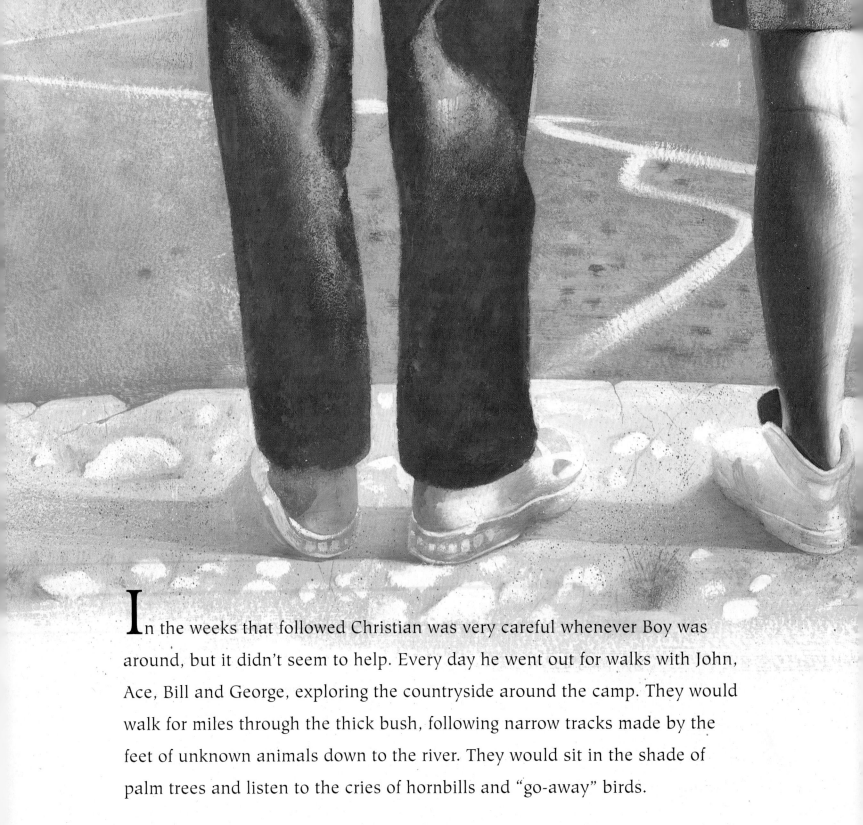

In the weeks that followed Christian was very careful whenever Boy was around, but it didn't seem to help. Every day he went out for walks with John, Ace, Bill and George, exploring the countryside around the camp. They would walk for miles through the thick bush, following narrow tracks made by the feet of unknown animals down to the river. They would sit in the shade of palm trees and listen to the cries of hornbills and "go-away" birds.

They would climb to the top of the great round rocks that rose high over
George's camp and look out across the African landscape - a sea of grey trees
and thorn bushes that stretched into the distance, towards the thin green line
of the river. But even though every day was a marvellous adventure for
Christian, he would return to camp only to be met by Boy's dark looks and
brooding anger.

"It's no use," said George one day. "Boy's not letting up. The only thing to do is take them both to an open space and allow them to meet face to face."

The next day no one mentioned Boy and when they set off on Christian's daily walk everything seemed normal. But, instead of heading for the river as usual, George led everyone straight up onto one of the high rocks.

Christian loved the rocks. He loved the cool wind that blew across them. But today the wind carried a different smell, a frightening, familiar scent that got stronger and stronger.

When Boy finally appeared Christian knew that the time had come to be brave. He did not try to run, instead he lay on his front trying to look as small and meek as possible.

The air seemed to shake and shiver as Boy, his growls growing to a roar, moved closer. Then suddenly it happened - Boy's massive paws cuffed Christian's head left and right, left and right, his powerful jaws with their great teeth just inches away from the young lion's head.

In a few seconds it was all over. Boy ambled arrogantly off, breathing heavily but with his head held high. Christian stayed where he was, heart pounding, hurt in spirit but, amazingly, not in body. He knew Boy could have wounded him, even killed him, but he had used neither his claws nor his teeth. Instead, he had followed the law of the wild - telling Christian who was in charge but without harming him in any way.

The young lion brought himself to look across at Boy, now standing proudly on the highest point of the rocks, and the great beast turned his head slightly to acknowledge his junior, as if in recognition that he had taken his lesson well.

And he had. Soon the two lions had become great companions. Now Christian accompanied Boy, not George, on his daily outings. Boy taught him all about life in the bush, the animals that lived there, where to find water even in the hottest weather and, just as important, how to find and hunt food.

As time passed, Christian began to leave the camp more often. Even though both he and Boy would come back to visit from time to time, they were often gone for days on end. It wasn't that Christian had forgotten his human friends, rather that he had remembered how to be a lion again.

Journey to Freedom

Ace, John and Bill had also left the camp and returned to England. But a year later they decided to pay George a visit and see how their "cub" was faring. Wondering if Christian would remember them after all this time, they were led by George up onto the same great rocks where Christian had received his first lesson in the laws of nature.

Halfway up, on a level piece of ground, George began to call and soon, reluctantly and slowly, Christian came strolling down the hillside. He was still some distance away when he raised his head to sniff the wind. His careful walk began to quicken and then, with a face that seemed almost to smile, he broke into a great loping run towards them. Although he was now a magnificent fully-grown male lion, Christian greeted his old friends just as he had when he was a little cub, jumping up to hold and lick them in a display of true affection.

It was a moment that no-one who had watched it - neither John nor Ace, Bill nor George - would ever forget. This wild lion that they had returned to the harsh bush of Africa still remembered them - no, more than that, remembered them with obvious love.

And that brings us at last to the end of Christian's journey - from a pet department to a furniture shop, a caravan in the English countryside to George's camp, and finally to his true home in the African bush. He may have been born in a zoo but his spirit was born free and that's exactly how he lived for the rest of his life.

A true journey to freedom - Christian's travels would take him from the streets of London to the wide open plains of Africa.

In the late 1950's a remarkable story caught the imagination of the world. Two people, George and Joy Adamson, decided to try and return a little lion cub to the wild. People said it couldn't be done but, *Born Free*, the true story of Elsa, the lioness of two worlds, proved that it could — it also changed the way that people looked at lions forever. Twelve years later it seemed that history was about to repeat itself...

THE **REAL** STORY

Christian embarks on his long journey to Africa (above).
After a long day exploring his new home at George Adamson's
Kenyan camp. Christian takes a well-deserved nap with his
friend Ace (right)...

Into Africa

Months passed and eventually everything was ready for
Christian's epic journey. The Kenyan government had agreed
to Christian's reintroduction as long as it took place in a
remote location where no people lived. After months of
looking, George had settled on Kora in north-eastern Kenya
and the all-important permits had been issued. Meanwhile,
Ace and John had been busy introducing Christian to his
travelling crate so that he wouldn't be too nervous when the
great day eventually arrived.

Christian was duly loaded into the crate, into a truck and
finally onto a jet bound for Nairobi airport.

The change for Christian must have been immense — Africa
looked, smelled and sounded so different from the England
he was used to, but George, who was waiting for his arrival,
helped to put him at ease.

Then began the long, dusty journey to George's camp among
the dry thorn lands of Kora.

Lion in residence

When Christian arrived at the camp he was in for a surprise
— he wasn't the only lion around! Boy, a massive male lion
who had starred in the film Born Free, was already in
residence. Although he lived on the outside of the camp's wire
fence and Christian remained inside, Boy did not like sharing
his territory with this newcomer and made his feelings plain.
For several weeks George tried to get Boy and Christian to
accept each other, but the situation was only finally resolved
when the two were allowed to meet face to face and Boy
asserted his authority in a short but terrifying fight.

Back to the wild

After that first scrap the two lions became companions,
successfully challenging the other wild lions that lived in the
area. Bill, John and Ace left Kora, and Christian went on to live
the life of a truly wild lion. He occasionally visited George's
camp but, together with Boy, he gradually established his own
territory and successfully mated with wild female lions.

A cub for Christmas?

Just before Christmas, 1970, a little lion cub was born in a small zoo in the West of England. For many reasons the zoo decided not to keep him so he was sold to Harrods, London's most famous department store. In those days Harrods was still renowned as the place where you could buy almost anything, even a lion cub! Today, thankfully, both the law and the management have changed.

As Christmas drew closer, two young Australians came across the little lion and couldn't bear the thought of leaving him behind in Harrods' pet department. So the two men, Ace and John, bought him and took him home to their pine furniture shop in London's fashionable Kings Road. They named him Christian.

A move to the country

Time passed. Christian grew, as did his friendship with his new owners who were beginning to realise that he couldn't stay with them in the furniture shop forever. Then one day Bill and I visited the shop. Ace and John recognised us from the film Born Free and told us all about Christian. We offered to help, suggesting that all three of them moved to the country to live with us while we considered Christian's future. They accepted, and within no time Christian was installed happily in the garden of our home in Surrey — now the headquarters of the Born Free Foundation.

After much discussion, we decided to try and return Christian to his rightful home in Africa. Our old friend George Adamson himself had agreed to help, but our mission wasn't going to be an easy one. Firstly we had to secure permission from the Kenyan government to bring a lion into the country, and Christian had to be prepared for his journey.

Ace introduces Christian to his travelling crate.

Bill, Ace, myself and John take Christian on a trip to the seaside!

A brief re-encounter

A year later Ace and John returned to Kora, anxious to see how Christian had adapted to his new life of freedom. Imagine their pleasure when he bounded down the hillside to greet them, a fully-grown male lion, happily surviving in his natural habitat.

Christian continued to live near George's camp at Kora for a further three years. Then one day he disappeared. George believed that he had crossed the nearby Tana River to establish a new territory and, although he never saw Christian again, he received reports of a lion that looked very much like Christian living for several more years in an area to the north.

The value of freedom

George Adamson always maintained that even a short life of freedom is of far greater value than a longer existence spent caged up in a zoo. Thanks to his help Christian had a taste of that freedom, a chance to experience life in the wild, to live the *true* life of the African lion.

Above.
We watch anxioulsy as Christian comes face to face with Boy.

Left. Christian begins to experience the life of a wild lion - freedom at last!

Established in 1987, by *Born Free* actors
Bill Travers and Virginia McKenna, the *Born Free Foundation* has
become one of the United Kingdom's most active and widely-
recognised animal welfare and wildlife conservation charities.
The Foundation's objectives are to prevent the needless
suffering of wild animals and to conserve wildlife
in its natural habitat wherever possible.
The BFF projects span the world – Canada, America, Kenya,
Tanzania, Ethiopia, Scotland and Romania – as well as wherever
the abuse of captive wild animals is to be found.
The BFF provides a unique programme of direct care for animals
in need, be it a rescued lion, otter, or chimpanzee, an elephant
family, wolf family or orca family, responding and raising money to
help individual creatures as well as running long-term
conservation projects. We also hope to encourage a wider
understanding of the problems faced by many animal species.

You can directly help us by adopting an animal
and/or becoming a *Born Free* member.
Become part of the *Born Free* team and make things happen!
We can't do it without you!